The Parable of
the Two Builders

Text copyright © Daniel Collins 1995

Published by
Barnabas
an imprint of
The Bible Reading Fellowship
Peter's Way,
Sandy Lane West,
Oxford,
OX4 5HG
ISBN 0 7459 3241 X
Albatross Books Pty Ltd
PO Box 320,
Sutherland,
NSW 2232,
Australia
ISBN 0 7324 0918 7

First edition 1995
10 9 8 7 6 5 4 3 2 1 0

A catalogue record for this book is available
from the British Library

Barnabas ™ is a trademark of The Bible Reading Fellowship

Printed and bound in Hong Kong

The Parable of the Two Builders

Jesus told this parable about two builders: a wise man wanted to build a house.

He thought about the different places he could build.

His children might like playing on the sand—but it was not very sturdy for building on.

So the foolish man started to build his house on the sand. He was very happy.

Soon both houses were finished.

That night there was a terrible storm and the river overflowed.

The house on the rock
could not be shaken by the
storm and it stood firm.

But when the flood struck the house on the sand it collapsed and was competely destroyed.

THE PAINTBOX SERIES

Available from your local bookshop or,
in case of difficulty, direct from BRF.